Maths

Up to Speed Practice

10-11+ years

OXFORD

UNIVERSITY PRESS

Great Clarendon Street, Oxford, OX2 6DP, United Kingdom

Oxford University Press is a department of the University of Oxford.
It furthers the University's objective of excellence in research,
scholarship, and education by publishing worldwide. Oxford is a
registered trade mark of Oxford University Press in the UK and in
certain other countries

British Library Cataloguing in Publication Data
Data available

978-0-19-274096-0

10 9 8 7 6 5 4 3 2

Paper used in the production of this book is a natural, recyclable
product made from wood grown in sustainable forests.
The manufacturing process conforms to the environmental
regulations of the country of origin.

Printed in China

Acknowledgements

The publishers would like to thank the following for permissions to
use copyright material:

Page make-up: GreenGate Publishing Services, Tonbridge, Kent
Cover illustrations: Lo Cole

Although we have made every effort to trace and contact all
copyright holders before publication this has not been possible in all
cases. If notified, the publisher will rectify any errors or omissions at
the earliest opportunity.

Links to third party websites are provided by Oxford in good faith
and for information only. Oxford disclaims any responsibility for
the materials contained in any third party website referenced in
this work.

Introduction

What is Bond?

The Bond *Up to Speed Practice* series is a new addition to the Bond range of assessment papers, the number one series for the 11+, selective exams and general practice. Bond *Up to Speed Practice* is carefully designed to support children who need less challenging activities than those in the regular age-appropriate Bond papers, in order to build up and improve their techniques and confidence.

How does this book work?

The book contains two distinct sets of papers, along with full answers and a Progress Chart:

- Focus tests, accompanied by advice and directions, are focused on particular (and age-appropriate) maths question types encountered in the 11+ and other exams. The questions are deliberately set at a less challenging level than the standard *Assessment Papers*. Each Focus test is designed to help a child 'catch' their level in a particular question type, and then gently raise it through the course of the test and the subsequent Mixed papers.

- Mixed papers are longer tests containing a full range of maths question types. These are designed to provide rigorous practice with less challenging questions, perhaps against the clock, in order to help children acquire and develop the necessary skills and techniques for 11+ success.

Full answers are provided for both types of test in the middle of the book.

Some questions may require a ruler or protractor. Calculators are not permitted.

How much time should the tests take?

The tests are for practice and to reinforce learning, and you may wish to test exam techniques by working to a set time limit. Using the Mixed papers, we would recommend that your child spends 50 minutes answering the 50 questions in each paper.

You can reduce the suggested time by 5 minutes to practise working at speed.

Using the Progress Chart

The Progress Chart can be used to track Focus test and Mixed paper results over time to monitor how well your child is doing and identify any repeated problems in tackling the different question types.

1 Read this and write it as a number.

> one hundred and fifty-eight thousand two hundred and four

_____

2 Write the number that is 1000 more than 282 450. _____

3 Use these four digits and the decimal point to make the largest possible decimal number between 20 and 30.

__ __ • __ __

Decimal numbers are whole numbers divided into tenths, hundredths and thousandths. A decimal point is used to separate whole numbers from decimals.

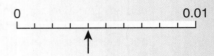

0   0.01

This shows thousandths.

0.004 is the same as $\frac{4}{1000}$

4 I'm thinking of a number less than 1. The two digits total 9 and it rounds to 0.2 to the nearest tenth.

What number is it?   0 . __ __

5 Write the missing numbers in these. Choose from **10**, **100** or **1000**.

28.09 × _____ = 2809

73.65 ÷ _____ = 7.365

0.072 × _____ = 72

6 Change this length from metres into centimetres and millimetres.

Metres	Centimetres	Millimetres
9.35 m	_____ cm	_____ mm

7 These are the heights of four boys. Write them in order, starting with the tallest.

If you need to put decimals in order, write them out one under the other, lining up the decimal points.

Adam   **1.22 m**

Ben   **1.29 m**

Charlie   **1.18 m**

David   **1.2 m**

_____ m   _____ m   _____ m   _____ m

8 Circle the smallest number and underline the largest number.

34.9   3.092   3.9   3.903   34.87   34.295

9 Write these in order.

9.405   **9.045**   **9.45**

_____ < _____ < _____

To round to the nearest tenth, look at the hundredths digit.

- If it is 5 or more, round up to the next tenth.

- If it is less than 5, the tenth digit stays the same.

Examples

4.86 rounds up to 4.9

2.614 rounds down to 2.6

10 Round each amount to the nearest tenth.

3.855 rounds to _____

17.806 rounds to _____

11 What is £46.38 to the nearest 10p? £_____

12 Round 235.48 m to the nearest whole metre. _____

Now go to the Progress Chart to record your score!   Total ( ) 12

Multiplication and division

Answer these. Show your method.

1   5 6
     ×   9
     —————

2   2 4
     ×   8
     —————

3   4 5
     ×   7
     —————

4 Circle the multiplication with the largest product.

56×43 53×64 46×54

With the grid method for multiplication, multiply each pair of numbers to complete the grid. Then add up each row to find the total.

What is 37 multiplied by 43?

×	30	7		
40	1200	280	→	1480
3	90	21	→	+ 111
			Total =	1591

5 Use this grid to multiply 58 by 26.

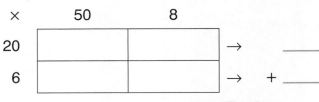

×	50	8		
20			→	_____
6			→	+ _____
			Total =	_____

6 Use this grid to help you multiply 358 by 30.

×	300	50	8
30			

→ = _____

Before working out a division, think about an approximate answer first.

Example: What is 659 divided by 4?

$$\begin{array}{r} 164 \ \text{r} 3 \\ 4\overline{)659} \end{array}$$

$$\begin{array}{r} -\ 400 \quad (4 \times 100) \\ \overline{259} \end{array}$$

$$\begin{array}{r} -\ 240 \quad (4 \times 60) \\ \overline{19} \end{array}$$

$$\begin{array}{r} -\ \ 16 \quad (4 \times 4) \qquad 659 \div 4 = 164 \text{ remainder } 3 \\ \overline{3} \end{array}$$

$$\begin{array}{r} 1\ 6\ 4 \ \text{r} 3 \\ 4\overline{)6_2 5_1 9} \end{array}$$

Complete these calculations.

7 $3\overline{)678}$

8 $5\overline{)297}$ r __

9 $4\overline{)985}$ r __

10 Circle the division that has a remainder of 3.

194 ÷ 5   306 ÷ 9   976 ÷ 8   295 ÷ 4

11 At a party, 75 glasses are needed for drinks. There are 6 glasses in a pack.

How many packs are needed so that there are enough glasses? _____

12 Beads are put on necklaces in sets of 9. How many complete necklaces can be made from 176 beads? _____

Factors, multiples and prime numbers

Factors are those numbers that will divide exactly into other numbers. Factors of numbers can be put into pairs:

Factors of 21 → (1, 21)   (3, 7)   21 has four factors.

Factors of 28 → (1, 28)   (2, 14)   (4, 7)   28 has six factors.

7 is a <u>common factor</u> of 21 and 28.

1 Cross out the numbers that are **not** factors of 24.

  1   2   3   4   5   6   7   8   9   10   11   12

2 Write the missing factors of 60.

  60 → (1, 60) (2, __) (3, __) (__, __) (__, __) (__, __)

3 Write the factors of 72 in order, starting with the smallest.

  _____

4 What are the **common factors** of 18 and 42?

  1, __, __ and __

A prime number only has two factors, 1 and itself. For example, 13 is a prime number as it can only be divided exactly by 1 and 13.

5 What is the next prime number after 20? _____

6 Complete these sentences with **always**, **sometimes** or **never**.

  A prime number will _____ have an odd number of factors.

  A square number will _____ have an odd number of factors.

7 Which two consecutive **prime** numbers multiply to make 77?

___ × ___ = 77

A multiple is a number made by multiplying together two other numbers. For example, the multiples of 3 are 3, 6, 9, 12, 15, and so on.

12 is a <u>common multiple</u> of 3 and 4 because 4 × 3 = 12

---

8 Circle the numbers that are multiples of both 6 and 5.

45   60   15   30   50

9 Write each of these numbers in the correct place on the Venn diagram.

35   60   42   56

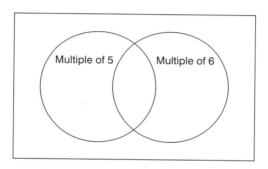

10 What is the smallest number that is a common multiple of 9 and 6? ___

11 Circle the square numbers in this set.

81   36   18   56   100   48   64

12 The next square number after 144 is 169.

True or False? _____

Focus test 4 — Fractions, decimals, percentages, ratio and proportion

Equivalent fractions have the same value, even though they may look different.

$$\frac{6}{9} = \frac{2}{3}$$

To write $\frac{6}{9}$ in its lowest terms it is simplified to $\frac{2}{3}$

Write the fraction of each shape that is shaded. Express each fraction in its lowest terms.

1

2

3

_____   _____   _____

Answer the questions about this rectangle.

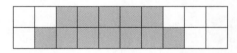

4 What fraction of this rectangle is shaded? Write the fraction in its lowest terms. _____

5 Circle the percentage that is shaded.

12%   20%   60%
    30%   15%

6 Shade more of the squares so that 75% is shaded in total.

7 Six pens cost a total of £2.40. What is the cost of ten of these pens?

£_____

To change fractions to percentages, make them out of 100. This means you need to find the equivalent fraction with the denominator 100.

Example

$\frac{2}{5}$ is equivalent to $\frac{40}{100} = 40\%$

To change a percentage to a fraction, make it a fraction out of 100 and then simplify it.

Example

20% is $\frac{20}{100}$ which is the same as $\frac{1}{5}$

8 Convert each of these fractions to decimals and percentages.

Fraction	$\frac{3}{5}$	$\frac{9}{100}$	$\frac{7}{20}$	$\frac{4}{25}$	$\frac{1}{2}$
Decimal	____	____	____	____	____
Percentage	____	____	____	____	____

9 Put the fractions from this chart in order of size, starting with the smallest value.

_____   _____   _____   _____   _____

10 Circle the smallest decimal and underline the largest decimal.

0.04   0.15   0.32   0.1   0.06   0.27

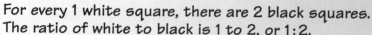

Ratio is used to compare one amount with another.

Example

What is the ratio of white to black squares?

For every 1 white square, there are 2 black squares.
The ratio of white to black is 1 to 2, or 1:2.

The <u>proportion</u> of squares that are white is 1 in every 3, or $\frac{1}{3}$

If this pattern was continued so there were 30 squares altogether, 10 would be white and 20 would be black.

11 A box of chocolates is filled with milk chocolates and plain chocolates in the ratio of 1:3. Complete the chart and then answer the questions.

Milk chocolates	1	2	3	4	5	6
Plain chocolates	3	6	____	____	____	____
Total		4	____	____	____	____

What proportion of the chocolates are milk chocolate? _____

How many plain chocolates are there in a box of 40 chocolates? _____

12 Sam mixes 1 litre of white paint with every 4 litres of blue paint. He needs 15 litres of paint altogether. How many litres of blue paint will he need? _____ litres

Now go to the Progress Chart to record your score!   Total   12

11

A sequence is a list of numbers in a pattern. You can often find the rule for a sequence by looking at the difference between the numbers.

What is the next number in this sequence?

58   49   40   31   22   __

Each number is 9 less than the previous one, so the next number is 13. The rule is 'subtract 9'.

1 Write the next number in each sequence.

14.5   15   15.5   16   _____

$\frac{1}{4}$ $\frac{1}{2}$ $\frac{3}{4}$ 1   _____

37   31   25   19   _____

2 Write the missing number in each sequence.

19   69   _____   169   219

8.7   7.8   _____   6   5.1

3 Write the rule for this sequence.

−13   −8   −3   2   7   12

The rule is _____

4 Will 50 be in this sequence? Yes or No? _____

5 Continue this pattern.

   1   4   9   16   25   36   _____   _____

6 What is the name for these numbers? _____

7 Write the next two numbers in this sequence.

   −9   −20   −31   −42   _____   _____

8 Write the next number in each sequence.

$\frac{1}{3}$ $\frac{2}{3}$ 1 $1\frac{1}{3}$ _____

$3\frac{3}{4}$ $4\frac{1}{4}$ $4\frac{3}{4}$ $5\frac{1}{4}$ _____

9 Write the missing numbers in this sequence.

   _____   14   34   54   74   _____

10 Write the rule for this sequence.

   17   9   1   −7   −15

The rule is _____

11 Write the next two numbers in this sequence.

   0.75   0.66   0.57   0.48   _____   _____

12 What are the next three numbers in this sequence?

   1   1   2   3   5   8   _____   _____   _____

Now go to the Progress Chart to record your score!   Total   12

Equations have letters or symbols instead of numbers in a calculation.

$2n = 12$

$\triangle - 3 = 8$

$\square + 4 = 10$

You use the numbers given to work out the value of the symbol or letter.

$2n$ means n multiplied by 2. The multiplication sign × isn't used in equations because it looks like a letter.

What number does each letter represent?

1 $12 - y = 8$ $y =$ ___

2 $5c = 15$ $c =$ ___

3 $\dfrac{21}{x} = 3$ $x =$ ___

Write the value of each letter in these equations.

4 $3c + 1 = 7$ $c =$ ___

5 $4n - 5 = 7$ $n =$ ___

6 $\dfrac{a}{2} - 3 = 1$ $a =$ ___

Answer these, for the following values:

$a = 4$ $b = 3$ $c = 5$

7 $3a + 5 =$ _____

8 $4b + 2c =$ _____

9 $5a + b + 3c =$ _____

> A formula uses letters or words to give a rule.
> (The plural of formula is formulae.)

P = perimeter

S = sides

S

We use the formula $P = 4S$ to find the perimeter of a square.

10 What is the perimeter of a square with sides of 3.5 cm? _____ cm

This table records the number of pencils in boxes.

Boxes	1	2	3	4	5	n
Number of pencils	4	8	_____	_____	_____	_____

11 Write the missing number of pencils on the chart.

Look at the chart and write a formula for the total number of pencils in each box. _____

12 How many pencils will there be in 50 boxes? _____

Focus test 7　Shapes and angles

Here are the properties of different quadrilaterals:

Square 4 equal sides 4 equal angles	**Rectangle** 2 pairs of equal sides 4 right angles	**Rhombus** 4 equal sides opposite sides parallel opposite angles equal
Parallelogram opposite sides equal and parallel opposite angles equal	**Kite** 2 pairs of adjacent sides equal	**Trapezium** 1 pair of parallel sides

1 Name these quadrilaterals.

_____　　_____　　_____

Is each statement true or false? Circle the answer.

2 A trapezium always has a pair of parallel sides.　True / False

3 A kite is always symmetrical.　True / False

4 A rhombus always has pairs of opposite angles the same size.

True / False

5 How many lines of symmetry are there on a regular octagon? _____

The net of a shape is what it looks like when it is opened out flat.　　*Example*　Net of a cuboid

6 What shape is made from this net?　　**7** Draw a net of a cube on this grid.

_____

8 Complete this chart.

Name of shape	Number of faces	Number of vertices	Number of edges
Cuboid	___	___	___
Square-based pyramid	___	___	___

9 Write the names of these shapes.

_____   _____

10 Calculate the size of angle *a* in this triangle.

Do not use a protractor.

Angle *a* = ___°

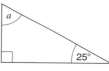

11 What is the size of the missing angle?

Do not use a protractor.

Angle *x* = ___°

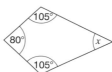

All the angles of a triangle add up to 180°.

$a + b + c = 180°$

All the angles of a quadrilateral add up to 360°.

$a + b + c + d = 360°$

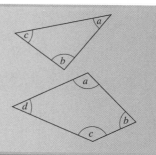

12 Measure these angles accurately with a protractor.

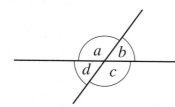

Angle *a* = _____°   Angle *b* = _____°

Angle *c* = _____°   Angle *d* = _____°

Focus test 8   Area and perimeter

Area is usually measured in square centimetres or square metres, written as cm^2 and m^2. Always remember to write this at the end of the measurement.

The area of a rectangle is length × width.

Example

Area = 3 cm × 6 cm = 18 cm^2

3 cm

6 cm

1 A rectangle has an area of 56 cm^2.
   One side is 8 cm long.

   What is the length of the side marked n?

   _____ cm

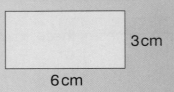

n cm

56 cm^2 8 cm

2 Draw a line between each pair of shapes with the same area.

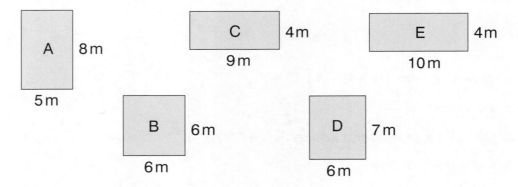

A   8 m
5 m

C   4 m
9 m

E   4 m
10 m

B   6 m
6 m

D   7 m
6 m

3 Calculate the area of this shape. _____ m^2

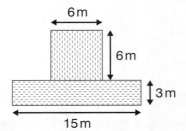

6 m

6 m

3 m

15 m

You can work out the perimeter of a rectangle by totalling the length and width and then doubling the total. Here is a formula for this:

2(length + width) or 2(l + w)

Perimeter = 2(6 + 4) = 20 cm

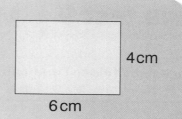

4 cm

6 cm

4 Draw a line between each pair of shapes with the same length perimeter.

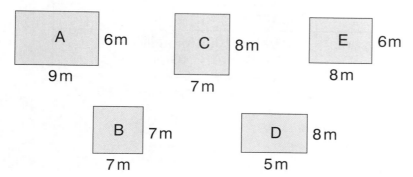

A   6 m
9 m

C   8 m
7 m

E   6 m
8 m

B   7 m
7 m

D   8 m
5 m

What is the area and perimeter of each of these rectangles?

5 Area = _____ cm^2

6 Perimeter = _____ cm

9.5 cm

6 cm

7 Area = _____ cm^2

8 Perimeter = _____ cm

35 cm

12 cm

9 A square has an area of 16 cm^2 and a perimeter of 16 cm.

What is the length of one side of this square? _____ cm

10 What is the area of a rectangular field that is 45 m by 100 m? _____ m^2

What is the area and perimeter of this square?

11 Area = _____ cm^2

12 Perimeter = _____ cm

6.5 cm

Now go to the Progress Chart to record your score!   Total   12

19

Focus test 9 — Measures

Length, weight (mass) and capacity are all measured using different units.

Length	
1 m (metre) = 100 cm (centimetres) = 1000 mm (millimetres)	1 cm = 10 mm 1 km (kilometre) = 1000 m

Weight	Capacity
1 kg (kilogram) = 1000 g (grams) 1 tonne = 1000 kg	1 l (litre) = 1000 ml (millilitres) 1 cl (centilitre) = 10 ml

Convert between units by multiplying or dividing by 10, 100 or 1000.

Examples

1350 mm = 1.35 m   0.65 kg = 650 g   680 ml = 68 cl

1 Convert each of these lengths to complete the table.

Metres	Centimetres	Millimetres
0.95 m	_____ cm	_____ mm
_____ m	1240 cm	_____ mm
_____ m	_____ cm	6800 mm

2 How many millilitres are there in 8.5 l? _____ ml

3 How many kilograms are there in 4.7 tonnes? _____ kg

4 Which is heavier, 6.85 kg or 690 g? _____

5 Write these lengths in order, starting with the shortest.

1.05 m   150 cm   105 mm   1550 cm

_____   _____   _____   _____

Shortest →

We sometimes use imperial units. These are measures that were used in the past. Try to learn these approximate values.

Length	Weight	Capacity
2.5 cm ≈ 1 inch	28 g ≈ 1 ounce	1 litre ≈ 1.76 pints
30 cm ≈ 1 foot	1 kg ≈ 2.2 lb	4.5 litres ≈ 1 gallon
1 metre ≈ 3 feet		
8 km ≈ 5 miles		

Circle the best answer for each of these.

6 Approximately how many pints are there in 4 litres?

3 pints   7 pints   10 pints   15 pints   18 pints

7 Approximately how many miles are there in 24 km?

3 miles   10 miles   15 miles   20 miles   30 miles

8 What is the approximate length in centimetres of a tie 10 inches long?

5 cm   14 cm   20 cm   25 cm   45 cm

9 What is the difference between the amount of water in these two jugs?

_____ ml

10 What is the total amount of water in these two jugs? _____ litres

11 A bus should arrive at 20:25 but it is 15 minutes late.

What time will the bus actually arrive?

Write the time on these two clocks.

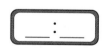

12 What is the difference in weight between these two parcels? Give your answer in grams.

_____ g

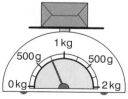

Now go to the Progress Chart to record your score!   Total (12

21

Coordinates are used to show positions on a grid.

Two numbers show the position. The number on the horizontal x-axis is written first, then the number on the vertical y-axis.

The coordinates of A are (–3, 4).

The coordinates of B are (–5, –2).

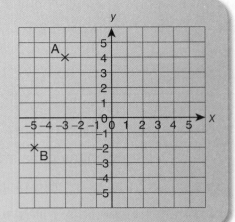

1 What are the coordinates of point A? (____ , ____)

2 What are the coordinates of point B? (____ , ____)

3 What are the coordinates of point C? (____ , ____)

4 A, B and C are three vertices of a rectangle. Plot the missing fourth vertex and label it D.

5 What are the coordinates of point D? (____ , ____)

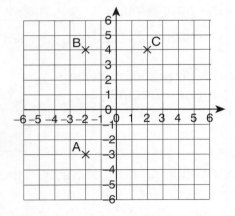

6 This is an isosceles triangle. What are the missing coordinates? Write them on the answer lines on the diagram.

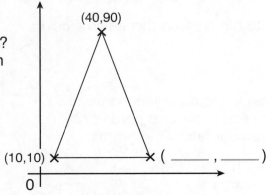

(40,90)

(10,10) (____ , ____)

A shape can be moved in three ways.

- Rotation: the shape is rotated about a point, clockwise or anticlockwise.
- Reflection: this is sometimes called 'flipping over'.
- Translation: this is sliding a shape across, up, down or diagonally, without rotating or flipping over.

Write whether these shapes have been **translated**, **rotated** or **reflected**.

7

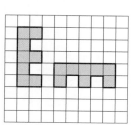

_____

8

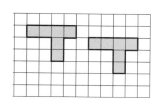

_____

9

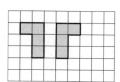

_____

This square is translated. Point B moves to (6, 5) and point D moves to (1, 0).

10 Plot A₂, B₂, C₂ and D₂ on the grid and join the points to show the translated position of the square.

11–12 Where are points A₂ and C₂ on the translated shape?

A₂ (_____, _____)

C₂ (_____, _____)

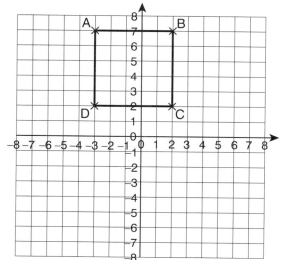

Now go to the Progress Chart to record your score!   Total ◯ 12

23

Charts, graphs and tables

This Venn diagram sorts the 26 letters of the alphabet.

Alphabet sort

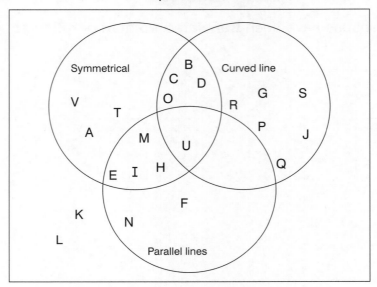

1 Write each of the last four letters of the alphabet in the correct place on the diagram.

W   X   Y   Z

Look at the Venn diagram and answer these.

2 How many letters have one or more **curved lines** and are also **symmetrical**? _____

3 How many letters are **not** symmetrical? _____

4 How many letters have both **curved** and **parallel lines** but are **not symmetrical**? _____

5 Which letter is **symmetrical** and has both **curved** and **parallel** lines?

_____

6 Which letters are **not symmetrical** and do **not** have **curved** and **parallel** lines? _____

To understand bar charts and other types of graphs, look carefully at the different parts of the graph before you look at the bars.

- Read the title. What is it about?
- Look at the axis labels. These give information about each axis.
- Work out the scale. Do the axes go up in 1s, 2s, 5s, 10s...?

The information from the Venn diagram has been drawn on a block graph.

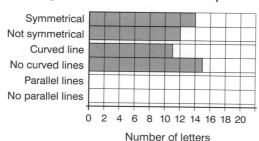

Sorting the 26 letters of the alphabet

7 Count the total number of letters with parallel lines and draw the missing block 'Parallel lines' on this graph. Remember, some will also have symmetrical and curved lines. Then, draw the missing block for 'No parallel lines'.

Use the information on the block graph to answer these.

8 How many letters are symmetrical? _____

9 How many letters have curved lines? _____

Pie charts are circles divided into sections. Each section shows a number of items so that they can be compared. You could be asked to give a fraction, a percentage or a number as an answer.

A bookshelf had 40 books on it. This pie chart shows the three types of books.

10 What fraction of the books are non-fiction? _____

11 What percentage of the books are fiction? _____%

12 How many of the books are poetry books? _____

Mean, median, mode, range and probability

- The <u>mode</u> of a set of data is the item that occurs the most often.
- The <u>median</u> is the middle number in a set of numbers when arranged in order.
- The <u>mean</u> of a set of numbers is their total divided by the number of items.
- The <u>range</u> tells us how much the information is spread. To find the range, take the smallest value from the largest value.

These are the number of goals scored by a football team over 9 matches.

  5   2   2   1   2   2   4   3   6

The mode is 2 because 2 goals were scored in 4 matches.

The median is 2 because 2 is in the middle when you arrange them in order:

  1   2   2   2   2   3   4   5   6

The mean is 3. A total of 27 goals have been scored. Divide this by the number of games to get the mean: $27 \div 9 = 3$

The range is 5. This is the difference between the largest and smallest value: $6 - 1 = 5$

These are the lengths of seven worms measured in a science lesson.

11 cm	11 cm
10 cm	14 cm
7 cm	9 cm
8 cm	

1 What is the mean length of these worms? _____

2 What is the median length of these worms? _____

3 What is the mode? _____

4 What is the range? _____

Another two worms are measured and added to this group.

5 cm 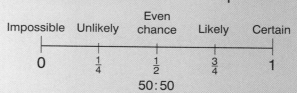   6 cm

5 What is the mean length of all nine worms? _____

6 What is the median length of all nine worms? _____

7 What is the new mode? _____   **8** What is the new range? _____

'Even chance' means there is an equal chance of something happening or not happening. We also say a 1 in 2 or $\frac{1}{2}$ chance, or a 50:50 chance.

Examples

What is the probability of rolling an odd number on a fair dice?

There are 3 out of 6 numbers that are odd (1, 3 and 5). This means there is a 1 in 2 or $\frac{1}{2}$ chance that it will land on an odd number.

What is the probability of rolling a multiple of 3 on a dice?

There are 2 out of 6 numbers that are multiples of 3 (3 and 6). This means there is a 1 in 3 or $\frac{1}{3}$ chance that it will land on a multiple of 3.

A probability scale can be used to show how likely an event is to happen.

Impossible	Unlikely	Even chance	Likely	Certain
0	$\frac{1}{4}$	$\frac{1}{2}$	$\frac{3}{4}$	1
		50:50		

Write the likelihood of the spinner landing on each of these. Write each answer as a fraction in its lowest terms.

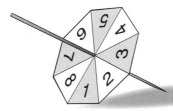

9 What is the likelihood of it landing on an even number? _____

10 What is the likelihood of it landing on a multiple of 3? _____

11 What is the likelihood of it landing on a number less than 7? _____

12 What is the likelihood of it landing on the number 1? _____

Now go to the Progress Chart to record your score!   Total   12

Mixed paper 1

Multiply each number by 1000.

1 8.2 _____   **2** 6.75 _____   **3** 91 _____

4 Write < or > to make this number sentence true. 0.518 __ 0.581

5 What is the total weight of two boxes weighing 14.6 kg and 5.5 kg?

_____

6 What is the difference between 483 km and 79 km? _____

Complete these calculations.

7 $5\overline{)283}$ r __   **8** $4\overline{)107}$ r __   **9** $6\overline{)390}$

10 Multiply 16 by 9. _____

11–12 Write the missing factors of 45.

45   →   (1, 45)   (3, ____)   (____, 9)

13–14 Which of these numbers are multiples of both 8 and 3? Circle them.

16   28   21   32   48   24   60

Change each maths test score to a percentage.

15 $\frac{45}{50}$ → ____%   **16** $\frac{32}{50}$ → ____%

Choose the correct decimal for each of these.

0.25   **0.2**   **0.52**   **0.5**

17 50% = ____   **18** $\frac{1}{4}$ = ____

Write the next number in each sequence.

19 4   2   0   −2   −4   ____

20 2.5   3   3.5   4   4.5   ____

3

1

2

3

1

2

2

2

2

21 767   667   567   467   367   _____

22 4   9   16   25   36   _____

Jamie built piles of bricks. Each new pile was a row taller than the pile before.

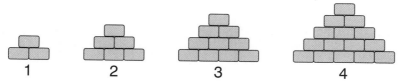

1   2   3   4

23–25 This table records the number of bricks in each pile. Write the missing numbers.

Pile	1	2	3	4	n
Number of bricks	3	_____	_____	_____	?

26 How many bricks will there be in the next pile of bricks in this pattern?
_____

27 What is the name of this shape? _____

28 How many lines of symmetry are there on this shape? _____

29 All the angles are the same size in this shape.
Circle the word that describes these angles.

reflex   acute   right   obtuse

30 How many pairs of parallel sides are there on this shape? _____

31 Draw a line to join the two shapes with the same size area.

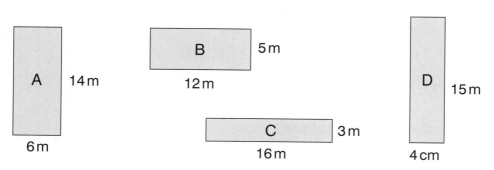

A   14 m   6 m

B   5 m   12 m

C   3 m   16 m

D   15 m   4 cm

32 Tick the two shapes with the same length perimeter.

33 A rectangle has an area of 63 cm². One side is 7 cm long. What is the length of the side marked x? _____ cm

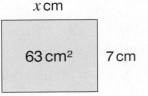

x cm

63 cm² 7 cm

○ 1

34 Calculate the area of this whole shape. _____ m²

4 m

7 m

5 m

8 m

○ 1

35 What is the length of this line in millimetres? _____ mm

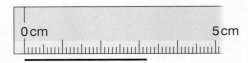

0 cm   5 cm

○ 1

36 What is the weight of this parcel? _____ kg

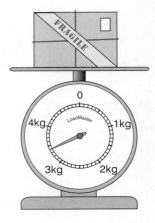

○ 1

Write <, > or = to make these statements true.

37 1700 ml ___ 1.7 litres

38 4.5 kg ___ 450 g

○ 2

Any answer that requires units of measurement should be marked wrong if the correct units have not been included.

Focus test 1

1. 158 204
2. 283 450
3. 28.61
4. 0.18
5. 100, 10, 1000
6. 935 cm, 9350 mm
7. 1.29 m, 1.22 m, 1.2 m, 1.18 m
8. (3.092), 34.9
9. 9.045 < 9.405 < 9.45
10. 3.9, 17.8
11. £46.40
12. 235 m

Focus test 2

1. 504
2. 192
3. 315
4. 53 × 64
5. 1508
6. 10 740
7. 226
8. 59 r 2
9. 246 r 1
10. 295 ÷ 4
11. 13
12. 19

Focus test 3

1. not factors of 24: 5, 7, 9, 10, 11
2. (1, 60) (2, **30**) (3, **20**) (**4**, **15**) (**5**, **12**) (**6**, **10**)
3. 1, 2, 3, 4, 6, 8, 9, 12, 18, 24, 36, 72
4. 1, **2**, **3** and **6**
5. 23
6. never, always
7. 7 × 11
8. 30, 60
9.

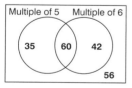

10. 18
11. 81, 36, 100, 64
12. True

Focus test 4

1. $\frac{3}{4}$
2. $\frac{5}{6}$
3. $\frac{2}{5}$
4. $\frac{3}{5}$

5. 60%
6. *Check another* **three** *squares have been shaded.*
7. £4
8.

Fraction	$\frac{3}{5}$	$\frac{9}{100}$	$\frac{7}{20}$	$\frac{4}{25}$	$\frac{1}{2}$
Decimal	0.6	0.09	0.35	0.16	0.5
Percentage	60%	9%	35%	16%	50%

9. $\frac{9}{100}, \frac{4}{25}, \frac{7}{20}, \frac{1}{2}, \frac{3}{5}$
10. (0.04), 0.32

Milk chocolates	1	2	3	4	5	6
Plain chocolates	3	6	9	12	15	18
Total	4	8	12	16	20	24

11. $\frac{1}{4}$, 30
12. 12 litres

Focus test 5

1. 16.5, $1\frac{1}{4}$, 13
2. 119, 6.9
3. The rule is add 5.
4. No
5. 49, 64
6. square numbers
7. −53, −64
8. $1\frac{2}{3}, 5\frac{3}{4}$
9. −6, 94
10. The rule is subtract 8.
11. 0.39, 0.3
12. 13, 21, 34

Focus test 6

1. $y = 4$
2. $c = 3$
3. $x = 7$
4. $c = 2$
5. $n = 3$
6. $a = 8$
7. 17
8. 22
9. 38
10. 14 cm
11.

Boxes	1	2	3	4	5
Number of pencils	4	8	12	16	20

   $p = 4n$
12. 200

Focus test 7

1. parallelogram, rhombus, trapezium
2. True

3. True
4. True
5. 8
6. triangular prism
7. *This is one possible solution. Check the net will fold to make a cube.*

8.

Name of shape	Number of faces	Number of vertices	Number of edges
Cuboid	6	8	12
Square-based pyramid	5	5	8

9. tetrahedron, hemisphere
10. Angle $a = 65°$
11. Angle $x = 70°$
12. Angle $a = 125°$, Angle $b = 55°$, Angle $c = 125°$, Angle $d = 55°$

Focus test 8

1. 7 cm
2. A and E, B and C
3. 81 m²
4. A and C, B and E
5. 57 cm²
6. 31 cm
7. 420 cm²
8. 94 cm
9. 4 cm
10. 4500 m²
11. 42.25 cm²
12. 26 cm

Focus test 9

1.

Metres	Centimetres	Millimetres
0.95 m	95 cm	950 mm
12.4 m	1240 cm	12 400 mm
6.8 m	680 cm	6800 mm

2. 8500 ml
3. 4700 kg
4. 6.85 kg
5. 105 mm, 1.05 m, 150 cm, 1550 cm
6. 7 pints
7. 15 miles
8. 25 cm
9. 450 ml
10. 2.95 litres
11. 20:40

12. 500 g

Focus test 10

1 $(-2, -3)$
2 $(-2, 4)$
3 $(2, 4)$
4

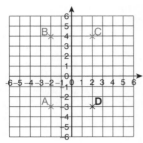

5 $(2, -3)$
6 $(70, 10)$
7 rotated
8 translated
9 reflected
10

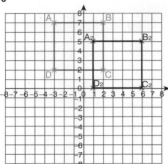

11–12 $A_2(1, 5)$ $C_2(6, 0)$

Focus test 11

1

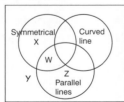

2 5
3 12
4 0
5 U
6 K, L, *Y*
7

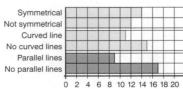

8 14
9 11
10 $\frac{3}{8}$
11 50%
12 5

Focus test 12

1 10 cm
2 10 cm
3 11 cm
4 7 cm
5 9 cm
6 9 cm
7 11 cm
8 9 cm
9 $\frac{1}{2}$
10 $\frac{1}{4}$
11 $\frac{3}{4}$
12 $\frac{1}{8}$

Mixed paper 1

1 8200
2 6750
3 91 000
4 <
5 20.1 kg
6 404 km
7 56 r 3
8 26 r 3
9 65
10 144
11–12 (1, 45) (3, **15**) (**5**, 9)
13–14 48, 24
15 90%
16 64%
17 0.5
18 0.25
19 −6
20 5
21 267
22 49
23–25

Pile	1	2	3	4	n
Number of bricks	3	**6**	**10**	**15**	?

26 21
27 hexagon
28 6
29 obtuse
30 3
31 *B and D*
32 *C and D*
33 9 cm
34 68 m²
35 32 mm

36 3.4 kg
37 =
38 >
39 (3, 1)
40

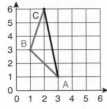

41 (2, 3)
42

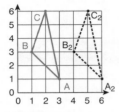

43 141–150 cm
44 40
45 30
46 151–160 cm
47 5p
48 15p
49 5p
50 49p

Mixed paper 2

1 840 m
2 107 m
3 8.26
4 10.95
5 44.1
6 60.4
7 8000
8 168
9 28
10 43
11–12 96, 24
13 True
14 False
15 <
16 >
17 20
18 15
19–20 4, 128
21–22 308, 558
23 8
24 36
25 57
26 9
27–29 Faces = 4, Edges = 6, Vertices = 4
30 Angle x = 130°
31 70 cm²
32 38 cm

33 81 cm²
34 36 cm
35 12 °C
36 −5 °C
37 1 h 35 min
38 3700 g
39–41

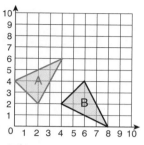

42 rotation
43 $\frac{3}{10}$
44 10%
45 80
46 20
47 unlikely
48 impossible
49 certain
50 likely

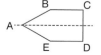
Mixed paper 3

1 10 g
2–3 (9.299), 29.3
4 £147
5 <
6 <
7–10

IN	270	150	300	240	600
OUT	9	5	10	8	20

11–12 4 and 9
13 29
14 20
15 1 : 3
16–17 Black → **20** tiles, Grey → **60** tiles
18 $\frac{5}{15}$
19 34
20 28
21 139
22 450
23 28
24 20
25 $a = 9$
26 $b = 3$
27 Line ED
28 Line CD
29 acute
30

B   C

A

E   D

31 121 cm²
32 44 cm
33

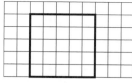

34 20 cm
35 1.2 litres
36 800 ml
37 8:35am
38 2:55pm
39 Shape C is a **reflection** of shape A.
40 Shape B is a **rotation** of shape C.
41–42 (3,4), (−4, 3)
43–44

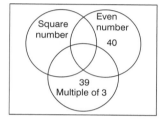

45 36
46 13
47 17
48 17
49 15
50 5

Mixed paper 4

1 753 006
2 751 906
3 753 000
4 753 906
5 £193.97
6 £6.03
7 7110
8 2776
9 1872
10 14 r 1
11 =
12 <
13–14 37, 29
15 $\frac{1}{3}$
16 50%
17–18 0.4, 5%
19–20 9, 4
21–22 481, 479
23 $m = 54$
24 $n = 9$
25–26 18 cups of flour, 6 eggs

27–30

	Pyramid	Prism
Shape letter	B C	A D

31 225 cm²
32 68 cm
33 144 cm²
34 48 cm
35 67 cm
36 900 ml
37 840 cm
38 3.8 kg
39 (−2, 1)
40

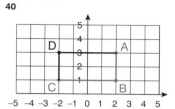

41 (−2, 3)
42 flag c
43 22 lb
44 5 kg
45 1 kg
46 6 kilograms
47 even chance
48 unlikely
49 unlikely
50 impossible

Mixed paper 5

1 26.5
2 349.1
3–4 5.03, 5.77
5 7352
6 3422
7 1794
8 5
9 £240
10 12
11 3
12 always
13 never
14 9
15 $\frac{3}{5}$
16 40%
17 >
18 <
19 6.5
20 $2\frac{1}{4}$
21 0
22 −30
23 11
24 37
25 $a = 27$
26 $b = 9$
27 False
28 Angle $d = 130°$
29 trapezium
30 4
31 114 cm²
32 120 cm²
33 A
34

35 2 litres
36 2 m

37 750 g
38 1.75 kg
39 translation
40 reflection
41 rotation
42

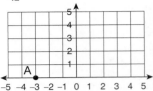

43 Washing clothes
44 60 litres
45 30 litres
46 330 litres
47 50 g
48 45 g
49 40 g
50 40 g

Mixed paper 6

1–4

Metres	Centimetres	Millimetres
6.4 m	**640 cm**	**6400 mm**
5.01 m	**501 cm**	**5010 mm**

5–6

```
    5 8 1
  + 2 7 9
    8 6 0
```

7 =
8 <
9 78
10 96
11–13 1, **2**, **7** and **14**
14 17
15 15
16 $\frac{10}{20}$ 17 $\frac{8}{10}$
18 20%
19–20 4715, 4775
21–22 0.2, 1
23 $q = 5$
24 $p = 2$
25 $y = 2$
26 $y = 4$
27 30°
28 60°
29–30 3 rectangles, 2 triangles
31 54 m
32 A and B have the same area.
33 2 m
34 7.5 m²
35 $\frac{1}{4}$ 36 $\frac{1}{2}$
37 $\frac{3}{4}$ 38 0

39 November
40 April
41 30
42 16
43–44 A (−4, 2), B (0, 6)
45

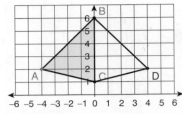

46 (4, 2)
47–50 30 mm < 3.2 cm < 32 cm < 2.3 m

Mixed paper 7

1 37.54
2–4 6.026 < 6.062 < 6.266
5–6

+	44	58
77	121	**135**
86	130	144

7 21 r 2   8 13 r 4
9 42 r 1   10 36 × 42
11 21   12 56
13 3 × 5 × 7   14 7
15 0.95   16 $\frac{14}{5}$
17 $\frac{10}{3}$ 18 $1\frac{1}{2}$
19 100   20 1
21 180   22 3819
23 $s = 11$ 24 6
25 $\nabla = 19$ 26 $g = 3$
27 parallelogram 28 Angle $a = 50°$
29 obtuse   30 scalene
31 15 m   32 12.4 m
33 A   34 12 cm
35 12 cm   36 14 °C
37 45 minutes   38 2750 ml
39 (−1, 2)
40–41

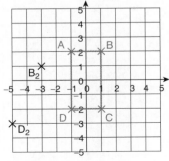

42 (−5, 1)

43 Amy
44 Matt
45 Evie
46 Kim
47 40
48 40
49 35
50 15

Mixed paper 8

1 1000   2 100
3 10   4 0.26
5 78   6 180
7 1168   8 975
9 1944   10 450 ÷ 8
11–12 3 and 14   13 36
14 24

15–18

Fraction	$\frac{3}{10}$	$\frac{7}{100}$	$\frac{2}{5}$	$\frac{4}{5}$
Decimal	0.3	0.07	0.4	0.8
Percentage	30%	**7%**	40%	80%

19 7.5
20 $2\frac{1}{4}$
21 1.5
22 0.5
23–24

Ring (r)	1	2	3	4	5
Squares (s)	8	16	24	**32**	**40**

25 $8r = s$
26 80
27 square-based pyramid
28 5 vertices
29 sometimes
30 Angle $x = 75°$
31 500 m²
32 3000 m²
33 90 m
34 240 m
35 650 ml
36 1.85 litres
37 <
38 10
39 A (−4, −1)
40 C (0, 2)
41 T (6, −1)
42 reflection
43 3 km
44 2 km
45 3:00–3:30pm
46 4:15pm
47 $\frac{1}{2}$
48 $\frac{1}{4}$
49 $\frac{3}{4}$
50 0

39 Write the coordinates of point A. (___, ___)

40 Plot C at (2, 6) and draw lines from B to C and A to C to complete the triangle.

41 Circle the coordinates that will be inside this triangle.

(4, 2)   (2, 1)   (3, 2)

(1, 4)   (2, 3)   (1, 2)

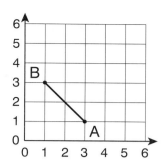

42 Translate this triangle 3 squares to the right. Draw the triangle in the new position.

(4)

The children in a school measured their heights to the nearest centimetre. This chart shows the range of their heights.

43 What range of height were most children? _____

44 How many children were over 150 cm high? _____

45 How many more children were between 131–140 cm than were 130 cm or under? _____

46 Underline the correct height group for a child that is 160 cm tall.

151–160 cm   over 160 cm

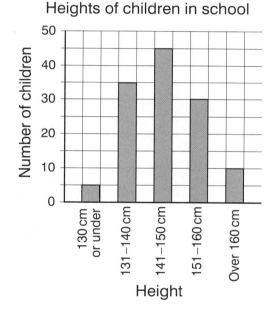

Heights of children in school

(4)

47 What coin value is the mode? _____

48 What is the mean value of the coins? _____

49 Which coin value is the median? _____

50 What is the range? _____

(4)

Mixed paper 2

Round each distance to the nearest whole metre.

1 839.5 m _____

2 107.48 m _____

2

Complete these calculations.

3 826 ÷ 100 = _____

4 1095 ÷ 100 = _____

2

Complete these calculations.

5
$$\begin{array}{r} 5\,2\,.\,6 \\ -\quad 8\,.\,5 \\ \hline \end{array}$$

6
$$\begin{array}{r} 7\,5\,.\,3 \\ -\,1\,4\,.\,9 \\ \hline \end{array}$$

2

7 20 × 400 = _____

8 8 × 21 = _____

9 196 ÷ 7 = _____

10 258 ÷ 6 = _____

4

11–12 Circle the numbers that are multiples of 8.

62   96   78   46   24   30

2

Is each statement true or false? Circle the answer.

13 17 is a factor of 68.   True / False

14 74 is a multiple of 6.   True / False

2

Write <, > or = to make each statement true.

15 $\frac{4}{5}$ ___ $\frac{9}{10}$

16 $\frac{3}{4}$ ___ $\frac{2}{3}$

2

17 Gina has collected 1p and 2p coins. There are 30 coins in total and $\frac{2}{3}$ are 1p coins. How many 1p coins does Gina have? _____

1

18 Jake mixes 1 spoon of fruit with every 5 spoons of yoghurt. For breakfast he has 3 spoons of fruit. How many spoons of yoghurt does he have? _____

1

Write the missing numbers in these sequences.

19–20 _____   8   16   32   64   _____

21–22 _____   358   408   458   508   _____   **4**

Write the missing numbers in these equations.

23 $23 + \underline{\hspace{1cm}} = 31$ **24** $\underline{\hspace{1cm}} \div 4 = 9$

25 $\underline{\hspace{1cm}} - 25 = 32$ **26** $5 \times \underline{\hspace{1cm}} = 45$ **4**

Write the number of faces, edges and vertices on a tetrahedron.

27–29 Faces = _____   Edges = _____   Vertices = _____   **3**

30 Use a protractor to measure this angle. Angle x = _____ °   **1**

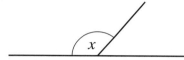

Calculate the area and perimeter of each of these.

   5 cm

14 cm

   9 cm

31 Area = _____ cm²   **33** Area = _____ cm²

32 Perimeter = _____ cm   **34** Perimeter = _____ cm   **4**

Write the temperature shown on each thermometer.

35

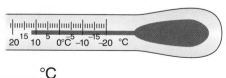

_____ °C

36

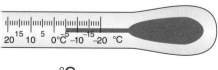

_____ °C   **2**

37 A film starts at 19:30 and ends at 21:05. How long does the film last?
_____ h _____ min   **1**

38 What is 3.7 kg in grams? _____ g   **1**

39–41 Draw another triangle at the following coordinates: (4, 2) (6, 4) (8, 0). Label it B.

42 Is triangle B a **translation**, **rotation** or **reflection** of triangle A? _____

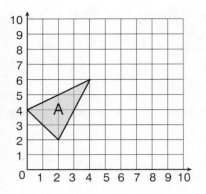

4

This pie chart shows the result of a traffic survey. There was a total of 200 vehicles in the survey.

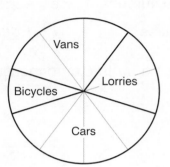

43 What fraction of the traffic were vans? _____

44 What percentage of the traffic were bicycles?

_____

45 How many cars were there? _____

46 How many more vans than lorries were there?

_____

4

Underline the chance for each of these.

47 What is the chance you will see a hot air balloon today?

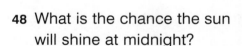

48 What is the chance the sun will shine at midnight?

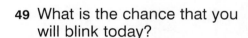

49 What is the chance that you will blink today?

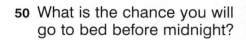

50 What is the chance you will go to bed before midnight?

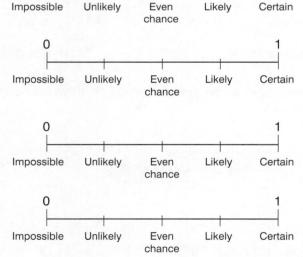

4

Mixed paper 3

1 A plum weighs 58 g. Would you estimate the weight of other plums to the nearest **10 g**, **100 g** or **1000 g**? _____

2–3 Circle the smallest number and underline the largest number.

23.9   9.392   23.09   9.93   29.3   9.299

4 What is £146.55 to the nearest whole pound? £_____

Write <, > or = to make each statement true.

5 54 + 17 ___ 123 − 51   **6** 140 − 84 ___ 27 + 33

7–10 This is a 'divide by 30' machine. Write the missing numbers in the chart.

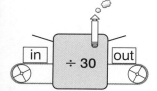

IN	270	_____	300	_____	600
OUT	9	5	_____	8	_____

11–12 Which two factors of 36 are missing from this list? _____ and _____

1   2   3   6   12   18   36

13 What is the next prime number after 23? _____

14 $10^2 \div \sqrt{25}$ = _____

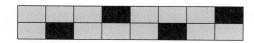

15 What is the ratio of black tiles to grey tiles? _____

16–17 This tile pattern is used on a floor that will need 80 tiles in total. How many of each colour tile will be needed?

Black → _____ tiles   Grey → _____ tiles

18 Circle the fraction that is equivalent to $\frac{1}{3}$

$\frac{3}{4}$ $\frac{5}{9}$ $\frac{3}{10}$ $\frac{5}{15}$ $\frac{4}{6}$ $\frac{3}{15}$

19 $3^2 + 5^2$ = _____

1

2

1

2

4

2

1

1

3

1

1

Write the missing number in each sequence

20 12   20   _____   36   44

21 145   142   _____   136   133

22 150   300   _____   600   750

Calculate these, when $r = 5$.

23 $23 + r =$ _____

24 $4r =$ _____

What number does each letter represent?

25 $34 - a = 25$ $a =$ _____

26 $6b = 18$ $b =$ _____

Look at this pentagon.

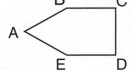

27 Which line is parallel to line BC? Line __

28 Which line is perpendicular to line ED? Line __

29 Describe the angle at A. Circle the correct answer.

right   acute   obtuse   reflex

30 Draw a line of symmetry on the pentagon.

What is the area and perimeter of this square?

11 cm

31 Area = _____ cm²   **32** Perimeter = _____ cm

33 Draw a square with an area of 25 cm². Use a ruler.

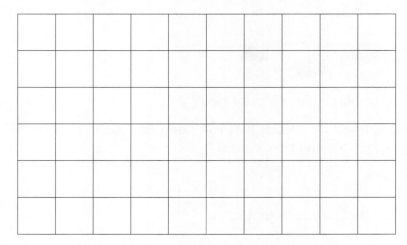

34 What is the perimeter of the square you have drawn? _____ cm

3

2

2

4

4

35 How much water is in this jug? _____ litres

36 400 ml of the water in this jug is poured into a glass. How much water will be left in the jug?

_____ ml

○ 2

Look at this clock.

This is the time a bus leaves the bus station in the morning. The journey to a school is 25 minutes long.

37 What time will the bus arrive at the school? _____

38 In the afternoon the bus arrives at the school at 3:20pm. What time did the bus leave the bus station? _____

○ 2

Look at the quadrilaterals A, B and C. Complete these sentences with **translation**, **rotation** or **reflection**.

39 Shape C is a _____ of shape A.

40 Shape B is a _____ of shape C.

○ 2

41–42 Circle the coordinates of A and underline the coordinates of B.

(3, −4)   (3, 4)   (4, −3)

(−4, 3)   (4, 3)

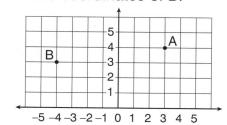

○ 2

The numbers 1–40 have been sorted on this Venn diagram.

43–44 The last two numbers are missing. Write **39** and **40** in the correct place on the Venn diagram.

45 Which number is a **square number**, an **even number** and a **multiple of 3**? _____

46 How many **multiples of 3** are there in total between 1 and 40? _____

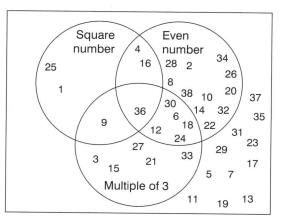

○ 4

These are Red group's spelling test scores.

Mike	Tanya	Will	Tom	Fay
17	18	15	20	15

47 What is the mean score? _____

48 What is the median score? _____

49 What is the mode? _____

50 What is the range? _____

○ 4

Now go to the Progress Chart to record your score!   Total ○ 50

Mixed paper 4

Read this number word and write all your answers using digits.

> seven hundred and fifty-two thousand nine hundred and six

1 Write the number that is 100 more. _____

2 What number is 1000 less? _____

3 Round the number word to the nearest 1000. _____

4 Write the number that is 1000 more than the number word. _____

○ 4

Mr Day bought two chairs for £39.49 each and a table for £114.99.

5 How much did he spend in total? £_____

6 How much change did he get from £200? £_____

○ 2

7 Use this grid to help you multiply 237 by 30.

×	200	30	7
30				→ _____

○ 1

8
$$\begin{array}{r} 3\,4\,7 \\ \times \quad 8 \\ \hline \end{array}$$

9
$$\begin{array}{r} 2\,0\,8 \\ \times \quad 9 \\ \hline \end{array}$$

10 Divide 99 by 7. _____

Write <, > or = to make each statement true.

11 3^2 _____ $\sqrt{81}$

12 $\sqrt{144}$ _____ 4^2

13–14 Circle the two prime numbers in this set.

51   37   49   29   35   27

There are 12 fish in a tank. 6 are orange, 4 are green and 2 are blue.

15 Circle the proportion of the fish that are green.

$\frac{1}{2}$ $\frac{1}{3}$ $\frac{1}{4}$ $\frac{1}{6}$

16 What percentage of the fish are orange? _____

17–18 Circle the two cards that show less than $\frac{1}{2}$.

$\frac{3}{5}$ 55%   0.4   5%   0.7 $\frac{6}{10}$

Write the next two numbers in each sequence.

19–20 49   36   25   16   _____ _____

21–22 489   487   485   483   _____ _____

Write the value of each letter in these equations.

23 $16 + m = 70$ $m =$ _____   **24** $3n = 27$ $n =$ _____

A recipe makes 10 biscuits using 6 cups of flour and 2 eggs.

25–26 How many cups of flour and eggs will be needed to make 30 biscuits?

_____ cups of flour _____ eggs

27–30 Write the letter for each shape in the correct section on this chart.

A   B   C   D

	Pyramid	Prism
Shape letter		

⟨4⟩

Calculate the area and perimeter of each of these.

25 cm

9 cm

12 cm

31 Area = _____ cm²

32 Perimeter = _____ cm

33 Area = _____ cm²

34 Perimeter = _____ cm

⟨4⟩

Complete these conversions.

35 670 mm = _____ cm

36 0.9 l = _____ ml

37 8.4 m = _____ cm

38 3800 g = _____ kg

⟨4⟩

39 Write the coordinates of point C.

(___, ___)

40 Line AB and line BC are two sides of a rectangle. Plot the missing fourth vertex and label it D. Draw lines to complete the rectangle.

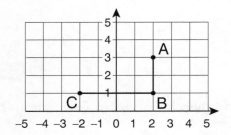

41 Write the coordinates of point D. (___, ___)

⟨3⟩

42 Circle the flag that is a rotation of the first flag.

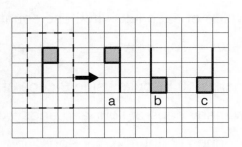

⟨1⟩

This is a conversion chart for changing kilograms to pounds, and pounds to kilograms.

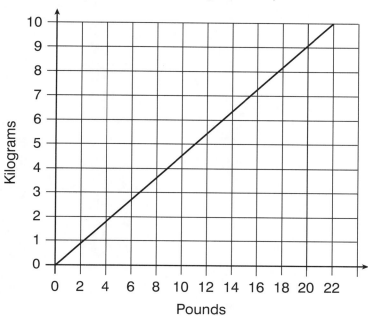

Conversion chart: kilograms to pounds

43 How many pounds are approximately the same as 10 kilograms? _____ lb

44 How many kilograms are approximately the same as 11 pounds? _____ kg

45 An old recipe uses 2 pounds of flour in a loaf of bread. Approximately how much flour would be the same in kilograms? Round your answer to the nearest whole kilogram. ___ kg

46 Which is heavier, 6 kilograms or 6 pounds? _____

○ 4

Underline the chance of rolling each of these.
What is the chance of rolling:

47 An odd number?

49 A multiple of 3?

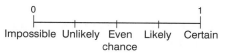

48 The number 1?

○ 4

50 The number 7?

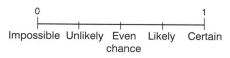

Mixed paper 5

Round each amount to the nearest tenth.

1 26.507 rounds to _____

2 349.061 rounds to _____

3–4 Write the numbers at each arrow.

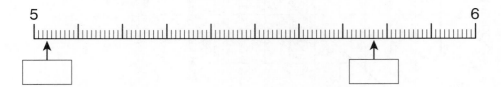

5 What is 5406 more than 1946? _____

6 What is 3778 less than 7200? _____

7 Use this grid to multiply 78 by 23.

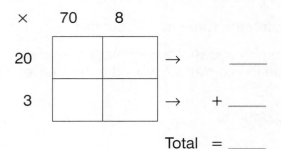

×	70	8

20 → _____

3 → + _____

Total = _____

8 Eggs are sold in boxes of 12. How many full boxes can be filled from 70 eggs? _____

9 A car needs 4 new tyres. One tyre costs £60. How much will it cost to replace all 4 tyres? £_____

10 There are 32 children in a class. Exercise books are sold in packs of 8. How many packs will be needed for each child to have 3 books? _____

11 What is the common factor of 12 and 27? _____

2

2

2

1

3

1

Complete these sentences with **always**, **sometimes** or **never**.

12 A prime number will _____ have an even number of factors.

13 A square number will _____ have an even number of factors.

14 What is the largest factor of 18, not including 18 itself? _____

Look at this rectangle.

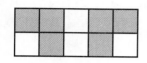

15 What fraction of this rectangle is shaded? Write the fraction in its lowest terms. ____

16 What percentage of this rectangle is white? _____%

Write < or > to make each statement true.

17 0.64 ___ 0.46

18 0.07 ___ 0.7

Write the next number in each sequence.

19 4.5   5   5.5   6   _____

20 $1\frac{1}{4}$ $1\frac{1}{2}$ $1\frac{3}{4}$ 2   _____

21 12   9   6   3   _____

22 10   0   −10   −20   _____

Calculate these, when $h = 7$ and $k = 8$.

23 $5h - 3k =$ _____

24 $3h + 2k =$ _____

What number does each letter represent?

25 $56 - a = 29$ $a =$ _____

26 $9b = 81$ $b =$ _____

2

1

2

2

4

2

2

27 This quadrilateral has no parallel sides.

True or False? _____

28 Calculate the size of angle d. Angle d = ___°

29 Circle the name of this quadrilateral.

      trapezium   kite   parallelogram   rectangle

30 I am a shape with 5 faces, 5 vertices and 8 edges. How many of my faces are triangles? _____

Calculate the area of each rectangle.

19 cm

A   6 cm

15 cm

B   8 cm

31 Area of A = _____ cm²

32 Area of B = _____ cm²

33 Which shape has the longer perimeter, A or B? _____

34 Draw a rectangle on the grid with a perimeter of 18 cm and an area of 18 square centimetres. Use a ruler.

35 A carton of fruit juice fills 5 glasses each holding 400 ml of juice. How much juice was in the carton? Circle the correct answer.

    1 litre   1.6 litres   2 litres   2.5 litres

36 A man is 6 feet tall. Approximately how many metres tall is this man?

_____ m

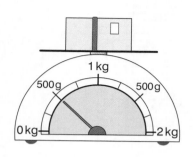 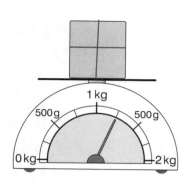

37 What is the difference in weight between these two parcels, in grams?
_____ g

38 What is the total weight of these two parcels, in kilograms? _____ kg

Write **translation**, **rotation** or **reflection** to identify how each pattern was made with the L-shaped tiles.

39 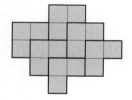 **40** 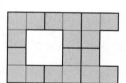 **41**

_____   _____   _____

42 Point A is at (−3, 0). Plot this point and label it.

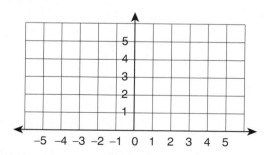

This block graph shows the amount of water a family uses in 1 week.

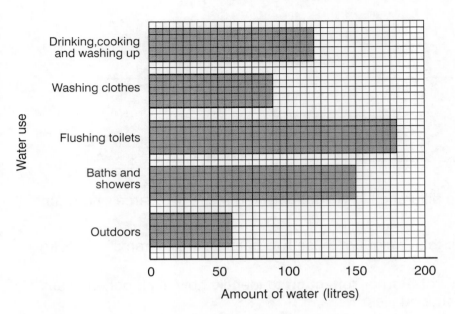

Family water use in 1 week

43 Which activity uses 90 litres of water? _____

44 How many litres of water are used outdoors? _____ litres

45 How much more water is used drinking, cooking and washing up, than washing clothes? _____ litres

46 How many litres of water in total are used flushing toilets and for baths and showers? _____ litres

4

These are the weights of nine oranges.

55 g   40 g   45 g   55 g   80 g   40 g   55 g   40 g   40 g

47 What is the mean? _____

48 What is the median? _____

49 What is the mode? _____

50 What is the range? _____

4

Mixed paper 6

1–4 Change each of these lengths from metres into centimetres and millimetres.

Metres	Centimetres	Millimetres
6.4 m	_____ cm	_____ mm
5.01 m	_____ cm	_____ mm

5–6 Write the missing digits in this addition.

```
  □ 8  1
+ 2 □  9
─────────
  8 6  0
```

Write <, > or = to make each statement true.

7 19×6 ___ 3×38 **8** $72 \div 4$ ___ $57 \div 3$

Solve these and write your answers as numbers not words.

9 Divide five hundred and forty-six by seven. _____

10 Share seven hundred and sixty-eight by eight. _____

11–13 What are the common factors of 28 and 70?

1, _____, _____ and _____

14 Which prime number is closest to 4^2? _____

15 What is $\frac{3}{4}$ of 20? _____

Complete these equivalent fractions.

16 $\frac{1}{2} = \frac{10}{\square}$

17 $\frac{4}{5} = \frac{\square}{10}$

18 There are 50 eggs in a tray and 10 are broken. What percentage of the eggs are broken? _____%

Write the two missing numbers in each sequence.

19–20 _____ 4730 4745 4760 _____

21–22 _____ 0.4 0.6 0.8 _____

Write the value of each of these letters.

23 $4q - 10 = 10$ $q =$ _____

24 $3p + 4 = 10$ $p =$ _____

What number does y represent in each equation?

25 $3y - 2 = 4$ $y =$ _____

26 $2y + 1 = 9$ $y =$ _____

Write the size of the missing angle in each of these triangles.

27

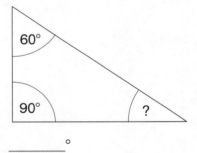

_____°

28

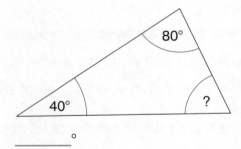

_____°

29–30 How many rectangles and how many triangles are there on the net of a triangular prism?

_____ rectangles   _____ triangles

31 A volleyball court is 18 m long by 9 m wide. There is a white line all the way round the court. How long is the white line? _____

1

4

2

2

2

2

1

48

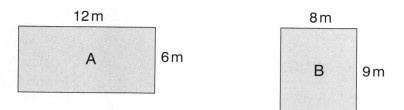

32 Underline the statement that is true.

A has a greater area than B.   B has a greater area than A.

A and B have the same area.

33 What is the difference in length between the perimeters of rectangles A and B? _____

34 What is the area of a rectangular pond that is 2.5 m by 3 m? _____ m²

All these shapes are placed in a bag and one shape is picked out at random each time and then replaced.

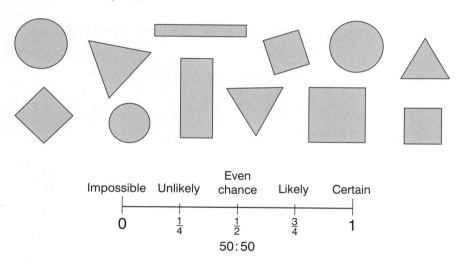

What is the likelihood of picking these? Look at the probability scale and write each answer as a fraction in its lowest terms.

35 What is the likelihood of picking a circle? ___

36 What is the likelihood of picking a quadrilateral? ___

37 What is the likelihood of **not** picking a triangle? ___

38 Circle the likelihood of picking a hexagon.

0   50:50   1

This graph shows the monthly sales of factual and fiction books in a bookshop.

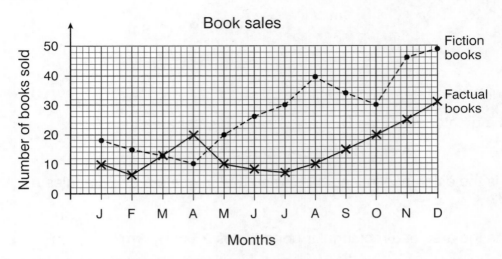

39 In which month were 25 factual books sold? _____

40 In which month were more factual books than fiction books sold?

_____

41 How many more fiction books than factual books were sold in August?

____

42 How many more fiction books were sold in November than in October? ___

43–44 Write the coordinates of A and B.

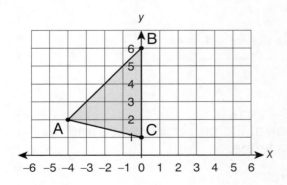

A → (_____, _____)   B → (_____, _____)

45 Draw the reflection of triangle ABC using the y-axis as the mirror line. Use the letter A_2 to label the reflection of point A.

46 Circle the correct coordinates of A_2.

(2, 4)   (4, 2)   (−2, 4)   (2, −4)

4

47–50 Write this set of measures in length order, starting with the shortest.

3.2 cm   **30 mm**   **2.3 m**   **32 cm**

_____ < _____ < _____ < _____

4

Now go to the Progress Chart to record your score!   Total   50

Mixed paper 7

1 Use these four digits and the decimal point to make the largest possible decimal number between 30 and 40.

__ __ • __ __

1

2–4 Write these in order, starting with the smallest.

6.062   **6.266**   **6.026**

_____ < _____ < _____

3

5–6 Write the missing numbers on this addition grid.

+	44	58
77	121	____
____	130	144

2

Complete these calculations.

7 $8\overline{)170}$ r ___   **8** $9\overline{)121}$ r ___   **9** $7\overline{)295}$ r ___

3

10 Circle the multiplication that has the largest product.

36×42 23×64 43×34

1

11 Which of these numbers has four factors?

21   23   24   25   28

1

12 Circle the number that is **not** a square number in this set.

36   64   16   9   56   25

1

13 Which three consecutive **prime** numbers multiply to make 105?

_____ $\times$ _____ $\times$ _____ = 105

1

14 Apart from 1, what is the common factor of 21, 35 and 84? _____

1

15 Which is the largest: $\frac{8}{10}$, **0.95** or **85%**? _____

1

Circle the improper fraction with the same value as the mixed number.

16 $2\frac{4}{5}$ $\frac{24}{5}$ $\frac{8}{5}$ $\frac{14}{5}$ $\frac{10}{5}$

17 $3\frac{1}{3}$ $\frac{13}{3}$ $\frac{10}{3}$ $\frac{9}{3}$ $\frac{4}{3}$

2

18 Write the missing fraction in this sequence.

$\frac{1}{2}$ $\frac{5}{6}$ $1\frac{1}{6}$ _____ $1\frac{5}{6}$

1

19 What is the next square number after 81? _____

1

Write the missing number in each sequence.

20 -3 -1 _____   3   5

21 45   90   _____   360   720

22 3829   3824   _____   3814   3809

3

23 What is the value of s?

$3s = 33$ $s =$ _____   1

24 Complete this, when $d = 9$ and $f = 4$.

$2d - 3f =$ _____   1

Write the value for each of these.

25 $61 - \nabla = 42$ $\nabla =$ _____   **26** $\frac{24}{g} = 8$ $g =$ _____   2

27 A shape has four sides. Each pair of opposite sides are parallel and the same length. The shape has no right angles and no lines of symmetry. Opposite angles are the same size. Circle the correct name for this shape.

trapezium   rectangle   parallelogram   kite   square   1

Look at this triangle.

28 Use a protractor to measure the size of angle a. Angle $a =$ _____ °

29 Circle the name of angle b.

right   obtuse   reflex   acute

30 Circle the name of this type of triangle.

scalene   equilateral   isosceles   right-angled   3

3.5 m

5 m

A   4 m

B   1.2 m

31 What is the perimeter of rectangle A? _____ m

32 What is the perimeter of rectangle B? _____ m

33 Which rectangle has the greater area, A or B? ___

34 What is the perimeter of a square with an area of 9 cm²? _____ cm

35 John is 158 cm tall and his dad is 1.7 m tall. How much shorter is John than his dad? _____ cm

36 What is the difference in temperature between these two thermometers? _____°C

37 A maths lesson starts at 9:50am and finishes at 10:35am. How long is this maths lesson? _____

38 How much water is in this jug? Write your answer in millilitres. _____ ml

39 Circle the correct coordinates for point A.

(2, −1)   (−1, −2)   (−2, −1)

(−1, 2)   (−1, 0)

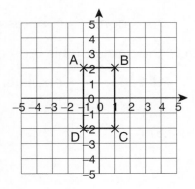

40–41 The shape is translated. Point B moves to (−3, 1) and point D moves to (−5, −3). Plot these two points and label them B₂ and D₂.

42 Where will point A₂ be on the translated shape? (_____, _____)

This graph shows how much pocket money each child gets and how they use their pocket money.

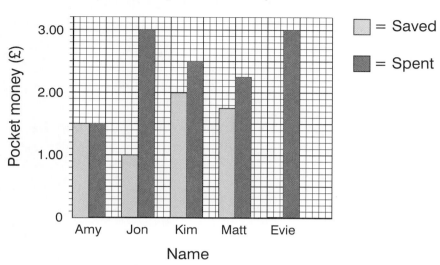

Pocket money saved and spent

43 Who saved the same amount of money as they spent? _____

44 Who got the same amount of pocket money in total as Jon?

_____

45 Who did not save any money? _____

46 Who got the most pocket money in total? _____   4

These are the number of pages in each chapter of a book.

Chapter	1	2	3	4	5	6	7
Pages	35	40	35	45	35	40	50

47 What is the mean number of pages in each chapter? _____

48 What is the median number of pages in each chapter? _____

49 What is the mode? _____

50 What is the range? _____   4

Now go to the Progress Chart to record your score!   Total   50

Write the missing numbers in these. Choose from **10**, **100** or **1000**.

1 $37.05 \times$ _____ $= 37\,050$

2 $940.7 \div$ _____ $= 9.407$

3 $8.118 \times$ _____ $= 81.18$

3

4 I am thinking of a number less than 1. The two digits total 8 and the number rounds to 0.3 to the nearest tenth.

What number am I thinking of? _____

1

Calculate these.

5 $92 - 14 =$ _____

6 $42 + 138 =$ _____

2

Multiply these.

7 $73 \times 16 =$ _____

8 $39 \times 25 =$ _____

9 $54 \times 36 =$ _____

3

10 Circle the division that has a remainder of 2.

$378 \div 7$ $615 \div 9$ $450 \div 8$ $381 \div 4$

1

11–12 Which two factors of 42 have a total of 17? _____ and _____

2

13 What is the smallest number that is a common multiple of 9 and 4?

_____

14 What is the smallest number that is a common multiple of 8 and 6?

_____

2

Complete the missing percentage, decimals and fraction in this conversion chart, giving the fraction in its lowest terms.

15–18

Fraction	$\frac{3}{10}$	$\frac{7}{100}$	$\frac{2}{5}$	$\frac{\Box}{\Box}$
Decimal	0.3	0.07	0._____	0._____
Percentage	30%	_____%	40%	80%

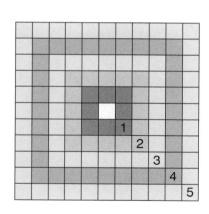

○ 4

Write the next number in each sequence.

19 1.5   3   4.5   6   _____

20 $\frac{1}{4}$ $\frac{3}{4}$ $1\frac{1}{4}$ $1\frac{3}{4}$ _____

21 0.7   0.9   1.1   1.3   _____

22 10.5   8   5.5   3   _____

○ 4

Look at this pattern that has been made from colouring squares on a grid.

In this pattern a 'ring' of squares is shaded around the centre square, which is blank.

23–24 This table shows the number of squares shaded in each ring. Write the number of squares that have been shaded on the 4th and 5th ring of this sequence.

Ring (r)	1	2	3	4	5
Squares (s)	8	16	24	_____	_____

25 Circle the correct formula for this pattern.

$8 - r = s$ $8r = s$ $8 + r = s$ $8 \div r = s$

26 How many squares will be shaded in the 10th ring? _____

○ 4

27 What shape will be made when this net is folded?

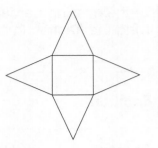

_____

28 When this net is folded, how many vertices will this shape have?

_____ vertices

29 Complete this sentence with one of the following:

always, **sometimes**, **never**

An isosceles triangle _____ has a right angle.

30 Calculate the size of angle x in this isosceles triangle. Angle $x = $ ___°

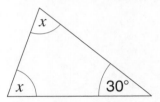

This is the plan of a house in a garden.

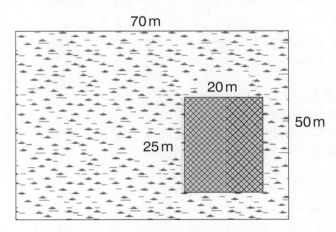

31 What is the area of the house? _____ m²

32 What is the area of the garden, not including the area of the house?

_____ m²

33 What is the perimeter of the house? _____ m

34 What is the perimeter of the garden? _____ m

35 What is the difference between the amount of water in these two jugs?

_____ ml

36 What is the total amount of water in these two jugs? _____ litres

37 Write <, > or = to make this statement true.

350 g ___ 3.5 kg

38 A brick is 30 cm long. How many bricks will there be in one row of a wall that is 3 m long? _____

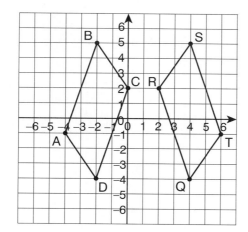

Draw a line to match each point with its coordinates.

39–41 Position A   Position C   Position T

(−2, 5)   (0, 2)   (4, −4)

(−4, −1)   (6, −1)   (−2, −4)

42 Complete this sentence with **translation**, **rotation** or **reflection**.

Parallelogram QRST is a _____ of parallelogram ABCD.

59

This graph shows the distance and time of Hannah's 10 km sponsored walk.

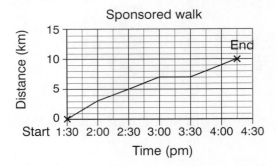

43 How many kilometres had Hannah walked by 2 o'clock? _____

44 How far did Hannah walk between 2:00 and 2:30? _____

45 Hannah had a half hour rest during the walk. Underline the correct time of Hannah's rest.

   1:30–2:00pm   2:00–2:30pm   2:30–3:00pm
      3:00–3:30pm   3:30–4:00pm

46 Approximately what time did Hannah finish the 10 km walk? _____

These are digit cards 1–12. All the cards are shuffled and one card is picked out at random each time and then replaced.

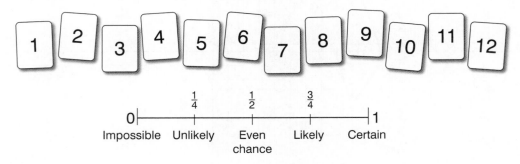

What is the likelihood of picking these? Write your answer as a fraction.

47 What is the likelihood of picking an even number? _____

48 What is the likelihood of picking a multiple of 4? _____

49 What is the likelihood of picking a 1-digit number? _____

50 Circle the likelihood of picking the number 13.

   0   50:50   1

Now go to the Progress Chart to record your score!   Total   50

60